A fire engine went by.

There was a fire.

Everyone ran to see.

"Get back," said a fireman.

A barn was on fire.

A little dog ran to the barn.

She barked and barked.

Floppy ran to the barn.

He jumped in the window.

"Get Floppy," said Chip.

The firemen pushed the
door down.

Floppy ran out.

He had some puppies.

Everyone looked at Floppy.

"What a good dog!"
everyone said.

What a hero!